SOMETHING UNDER THE BED IS DROOLING

A Calvin and Hobbes Collection by Bill Watterson
Foreword by Pat Oliphant

Andrews McMeel
Publishing, LLC

Kansas City • Sydney • London

Andrews McMeel Publishing, LLC
an Andrews McMeel Universal company
1130 Walnut Street, Kansas City, Missouri 64106

www.andrewsmcmeel.com

ISBN: 978-1-4494-0707-0

Foreword

There is a mystical quality to Bill Watterson's work. What we have here is no mere comic strip. It possesses a dimension which was found once upon a time in George Herriman's Krazy Kat and, later, in Walt Kelly's Pogo. That, however, was long ago, and since their passing, there has been nothing in the world of cartoon art to replace them. Now, we have Calvin and Hobbes.

There are no mealy-mouths or namby-pamby characters in this strip. The kid is delightfully and dedicatedly rotten. The mother and the father (no names are given or necessary) live alongside their offspring in a state of agitated wonderment at what they must have done to deserve this child. The kid, for his part, lives a good 70 percent of his time in a world I remember well from my own childhood, peopled with unspeakable creatures of the imagination, and the rest of the time in a real world peopled with other unspeakables (the teacher, the girl, the school thug). Refuge from the latter world is found in the former. And then there's the goofy stuffed tiger. A gentle soul, he is much smarter than the kid, whose brashness he leavens with a wry, endearing wisdom.

There are many comic strips out there, a few good, some average, a great many merely background clutter. All have their own cast of characters, engaging or not, all glued and patched together with dialogue, some good, some not. Very few bright stars appear who possess that peculiar magic which can provoke comparison with the best of the past. Looking at the work of our two comparisons, Herriman and Kelly, we can see a wedding of idea and art rarely seen these days, a feeling that words can enhance art and art can do the same for the written — that a carefully wrought blend of these ingredients can create a degree of enchantment which bespeaks genius.

You want magic?

Watterson the alchemist has conjured forth a work of subtlety, character, and depth far out of proportion to his tender years. I wish him long life, and may the powers of his sorcery never diminish.

You want magic?

This is a collection of the sorcerer's recipes for changing simple ink and paper into the purest gold. Humbly allow me to present Calvin (the kid) and Hobbes (the tiger). This book is magic.

— PAT OLIPHANT

To Mom and Dad

6

WITH A DRINK OF MAGIC ELIXIR, CALVIN TURNS HIMSELF INVISIBLE.

COMPLETELY TRANSPARENT, HE ROAMS UNDETECTED!

CALVIN?

BOY, AS SOON AS YOU WANT SOMETHING DONE AROUND HERE, THAT KID'S NOWHERE TO BE SEEN.

HA HA! I HAVE TURNED MYSELF INVISIBLE!

BY REMOVING MY CLOTHING, I CAN PERPETRATE ANY CRIME UNDETECTED!

I HAVE COMPLETE FREEDOM! I CAN GET AWAY WITH ANYTHING!

CALVIN! WHAT ON EARTH ARE YOU DOING IN THE COOKIE JAR WITHOUT YOUR CLOTHES ON?!?

YOUR POLLS ARE SLIPPING, DAD. BETTER GET WITH IT.

CALVIN, BEING YOUR DAD IS NOT AN ELECTED POSITION. I DON'T HAVE TO RESPOND TO POLLS.

NOT ELECTED? YOU MEAN YOU CAN GOVERN WITH DICTATORIAL IMPUNITY?

EXACTLY.

IN SHORT, OPEN REVOLT AND EXILE IS THE ONLY HOPE FOR CHANGE?

I DON'T LIKE THE DIRECTION THIS CONVERSATION IS TAKING...

I'VE DECIDED TO GROW A BEARD, MOM.

A *LONG* BEARD. LIKE THE GUYS IN ZZ TOP.

THAT'S NICE, CALVIN. YOU GO AHEAD AND DO THAT.

I THOUGHT SHE'D PUT UP MORE OF A FUSS THAN THAT.

WATTERSON

HOW ABOUT THESE PANTS, MOM? CAN I GET THESE?

GOOD HEAVENS, LOOK AT THE PRICE! *I* DON'T HAVE PANTS THAT COST THIS MUCH!

AND YOU'LL GROW RIGHT OUT OF THESE! HONESTLY, WHY WOULD ANY KID NEED DESIGNER CLOTHES??

"BABES."

BABES, MOM. I GOTTA LOOK COOL.

WATTERSON

23

24

TOMORROW WE'RE GOING TO DISCUSS "CURRENT EVENTS" IN SCHOOL.

EACH OF US HAS TO FIND A NEWSPAPER ARTICLE, READ IT TO THE CLASS, AND EXPLAIN IT.

WHAT ARTICLE DID YOU CHOOSE?

THIS ONE.

"SPACE ALIEN WEDS TWO-HEADED ELVIS CLONE."

ACTUALLY, THERE'S NOT MUCH LEFT TO EXPLAIN.

LOOK WHAT YOU CAN DO WITH BIG SOCKS!

JUST PUT ONE OVER EACH EAR, AND ONE OVER YOUR NOSE...

AN ELEPHANT! HA HA! I WANT SOME SOCKS TOO!

IF I MISS THE BUS, IT'S GOING TO BE UNPLEASANT AROUND HERE!

CALVIN, HOW DID YOU BREAK THIS DISH?!

I WAS CARRYING TOO MUCH AND IT DROPPED.

YOUR PROBLEM IS YOU'VE GOT NO COMMON SENSE.

I'VE GOT **PLENTY** OF COMMON SENSE!

I JUST CHOOSE TO IGNORE IT.

31

34

38

40

42

Panel 1: ARE YOU GOING TO COME TO MY PLAY, DAD? IT'S CALLED "NUTRITION AND THE FOUR FOOD GROUPS."

Panel 2: I'LL PROBABLY HAVE TO BE AT WORK, CALVIN.

BUT DAD, IT'LL BE GREAT DRAMA! I'M AN ONION!

Panel 3: WELL, WHY DON'T YOU SAY YOUR LINE FOR ME NOW?

OK! UM... ..LET'S SEE.. "IN ADDITION TO..." ..UH... HOLD IT... UM..

Panel 4: 25 KIDS IN FOOD SUITS, FORGETTING THEIR LINES. I'LL *DEFINITELY* BE AT WORK.

DEAR! CALVIN'S WORKED HARD.

OK, UH... "IN ADDITION.."..UH NO, WAIT.. UM...

Panel 5: DO YOU HAVE YOUR LINE MEMORIZED FOR THE NUTRITION PLAY, CALVIN?

Panel 6: I'M STILL LEARNING IT. BEING AN ONION IS A DIFFICULT ROLE, YOU KNOW. WHAT ARE YOU?

WATERSON

Panel 7: I'M "FAT."

NO, I MEAN IN THE PLAY.

Panel 8: ANYONE *ELSE* WANT TO SAY IT ?!?

AACKK! UNDERSTUDY! UNDERSTUDY!

Panel 9: THANKS FOR WAITING FOR THE BUS WITH ME, HOBBES. I FEEL LIKE AN IDIOT IN THIS ONION SUIT.

Panel 10: I'LL BE GLAD WHEN THIS STUPID PLAY IS OVER.

Panel 11: OH NO! RUN FOR YOUR LIFE! A PRODUCE TRUCK!

Panel 12: ...JUST KIDDING!

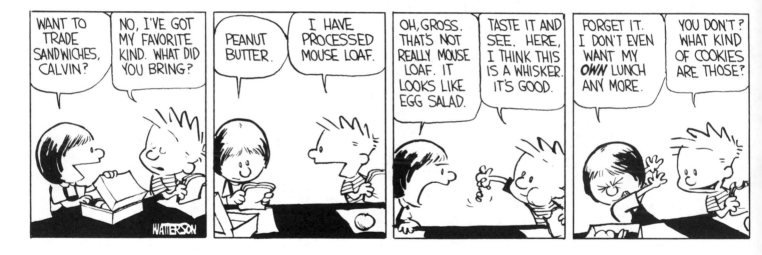

Row 1:

HOW DO THEY KNOW THE LOAD LIMIT ON BRIDGES, DAD?

THEY DRIVE BIGGER AND BIGGER TRUCKS OVER THE BRIDGE UNTIL IT BREAKS.

THEN THEY WEIGH THE LAST TRUCK AND REBUILD THE BRIDGE.

OH. I SHOULD'VE GUESSED.

DEAR, IF YOU DON'T KNOW THE ANSWER, JUST TELL HIM!

Row 2:

IT'S HARD TO BELIEVE PEOPLE STILL STARVE IN THIS WORLD.

THERE'S EVEN HUNGER IN AMERICA.

SOME PEOPLE NEVER GET ENOUGH TO EAT.

BOY, I KNOW WHAT *THAT'S* LIKE!

NO YOU DON'T.

Row 3:

THE SOLDIERS ADVANCE UP THE HILL!

OH, NO! A SQUADRON OF BOMBERS APPEARS ON THE HORIZON! THE BOMBS BEGIN TO FALL!

BONK BONK

TWO DIRECT HITS!

I SEE YOU UP THERE!

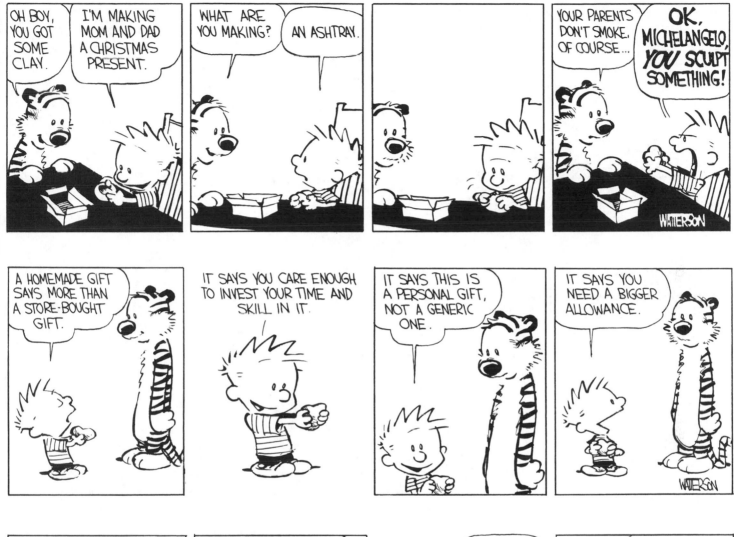

59

Row 1:

PSST! ARE YOU AWAKE?

IS IT CHRISTMAS? IT IS! IT IS!

LET'S GO WAKE MOM AND DAD AND OPEN ALL OUR LOOT!

SINCE IT'S CHRISTMAS, MAYBE WE SHOULD LET THEM SLEEP IN A LITTLE.

THAT'S LONG ENOUGH! WAKE UP! WAKE UP! IT'S CHRISTMAS!!

QUARTER TO 6. HE LET US SLEEP IN THIS YEAR.

Row 2:

OMIGOSH! THIS LIBRARY BOOK WAS DUE TWO DAYS AGO!

WHAT WILL THEY *DO*? ARE THEY GOING TO INTERROGATE ME AND BEAT ME UP?! ARE THEY GOING TO BREAK MY KNEES?? WILL I HAVE TO SIGN SOME CONFESSION???

THEY'LL FINE YOU TEN CENTS. NOW GO RETURN IT.

THE WAY SOME OF THOSE LIBRARIANS LOOK AT YOU, I NATURALLY ASSUMED THE CONSEQUENCES WOULD BE MORE DIRE.

Row 3:

HEY DAD, I HAVE A QUESTION.

SURE, CALVIN. WHAT DO YOU WANT TO KNOW?

IF YOU PLUGGED UP YOUR NOSE AND MOUTH RIGHT BEFORE YOU SNEEZED...

...WOULD THE SNEEZE GO OUT YOUR EARS, OR WOULD YOUR HEAD EXPLODE?

I WAS KIND OF HOPING YOU HAD A MATH PROBLEM OR SOMETHING.

...EITHER WAY, I'M SCARED TO TRY IT.

Panel 2: CALVIN, I HOPE YOU TOOK YOUR BOOTS OFF BEFORE YOU WALKED ACROSS THE FLOOR.

Panel 4: OF COURSE I DID! YOU DON'T NEED TO TELL ME ALL THE TIME!

GIVEN ANY MORE THOUGHT TO THAT BACKYARD SKI LIFT PROPOSAL OF MINE?

OH, YES. LOTS.

HOBBES IS ALWAYS A LITTLE LOOPY WHEN HE COMES OUT OF THE DRYER.

WATTERSON

—WHIFFFFF···

WHIFF · · WHIFF · WHIFF · WHIFF · WHIFF

FOR ALL THAT PREPARATION, YOU SURE ARE A LOUSY SHOT!

GO AHEAD DOWN. YOU'LL MISS ALL THOSE TREES.

YOU CAN DO IT. YOU'LL STOP BEFORE YOU GO OVER THAT LEDGE AT THE BOTTOM.

YOU WON'T GO INTO THAT POND. BESIDES, THE ICE IS PROBABLY REAL THICK ANYWAY. GO AHEAD DOWN.

MY BRAIN IS TRYING TO KILL ME.

GALOSH GALOSH GALOSH

73

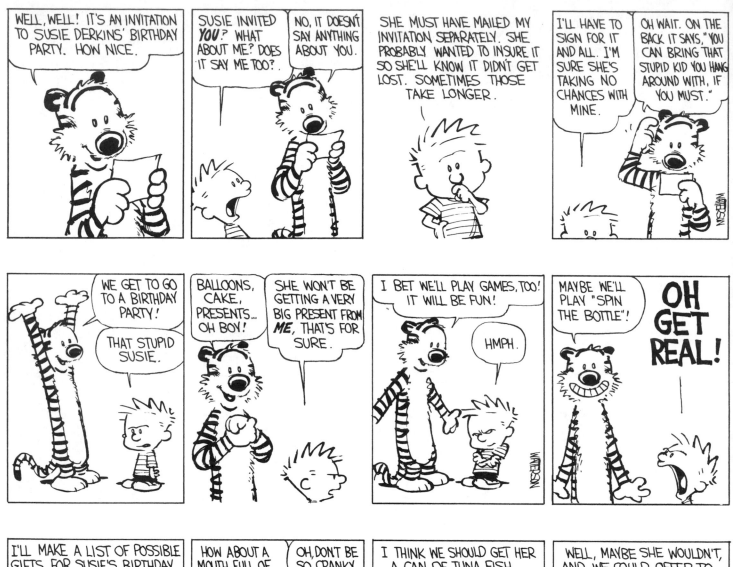

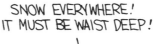

Panel 1: OH, MOM, I NEED SOME CRISCO FOR SCHOOL TODAY!

Panel 2: SHORTENING? HONESTLY, CALVIN, I WISH YOU'D REMEMBER THESE THINGS THE NIGHT BEFORE. NOW HURRY UP AND GET READY.

RIGHT.

Panel 3: HERE'S THE CRISCO BACK. THANKS.

YOU PUT IT IN YOUR *HAIR*??

Panel 4: GET BACK HERE! YOU'RE NOT GOING TO SCHOOL LIKE *THAT!*

AW C'MON, MOM! IT'S CLASS PICTURE DAY!

Panel 5: WHAT'S WITH YOUR HAIR?

Panel 6: I TOLD MOM I'M GETTING MY SCHOOL PICTURE TAKEN TODAY, AND SHE MADE ME COMB OUT THE CRISCO I PUT IN MY HAIR. NOW I LOOK LIKE A MORON.

Panel 7: THAT'S TRUE. YOU DO.

WELL DON'T JUST STAND THERE! THINK OF SOMETHING! WHAT CAN I DO?

Panel 8: THERE. MUCH BETTER!

WHAT'D YOU DO? IS IT COOL? IS IT NEW WAVE? GEE, I WISH I HAD A MIRROR...

Panel 9: THE BUS IS GOING TO BE HERE ANY MINUTE. YOU'RE SURE YOU FIXED MY HAIR SO IT LOOKS OK?

Panel 10: IT LOOKS GREAT. TRY NOT TO MUSS IT UP.

YOU'RE NOT KIDDING ME, ARE YOU? THIS REALLY LOOKS GOOD?

Panel 11: TRUST ME. YOU LOOK LIKE ... LIKE...

Panel 12: ..." ASTRO BOY."

ALL RIGHT! I CAN'T *WAIT* TO GET MY PICTURE TAKEN *NOW!*

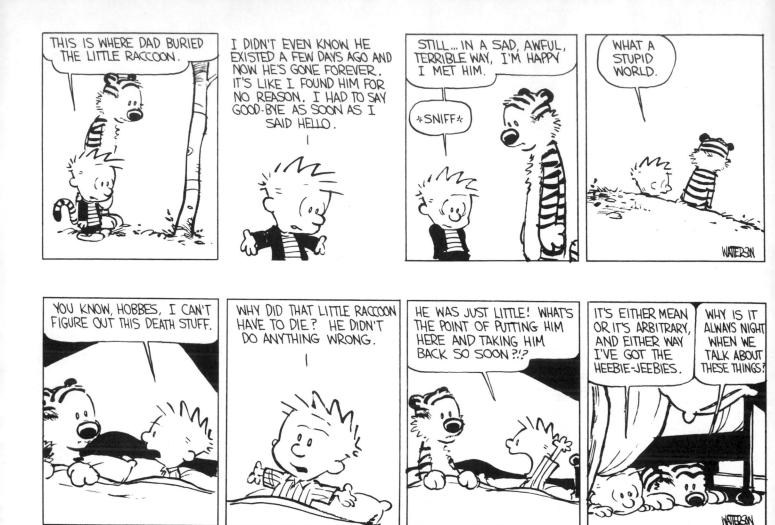

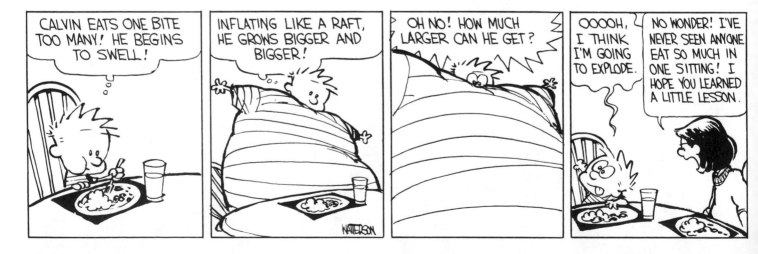

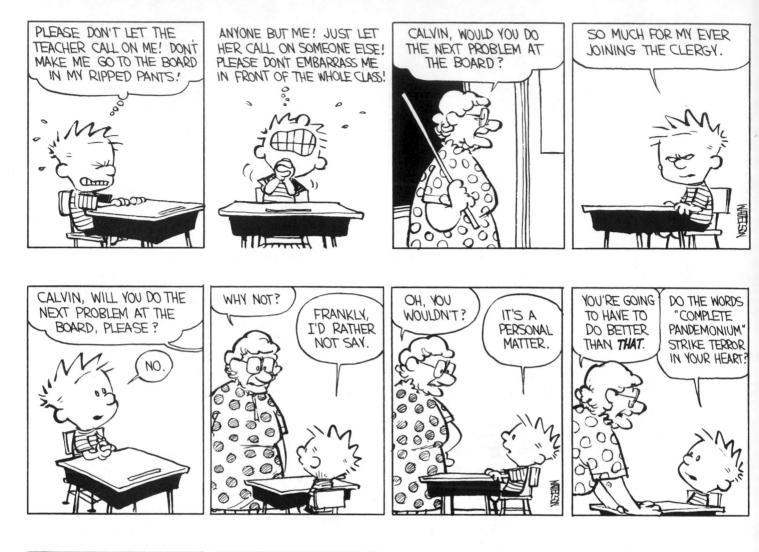

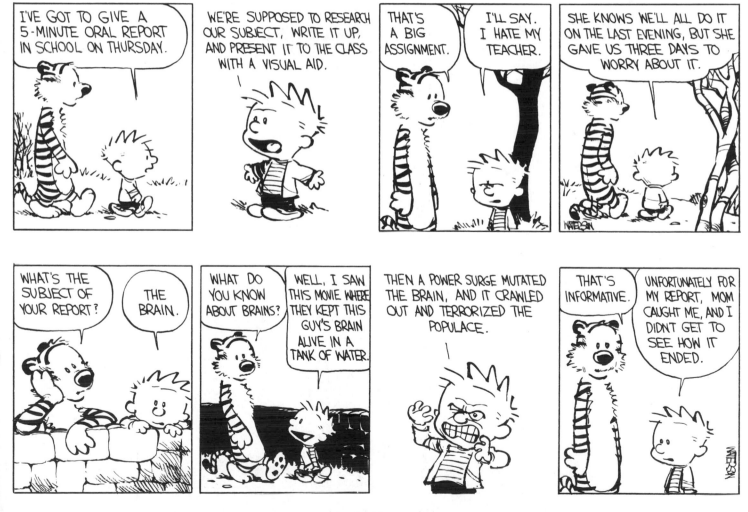

BOOK REPORT
"Treasure island"